gauguin

A BOOK OF SPECIAL DAYS

gauguin

A BOOK OF SPECIAL DAYS

Universe

Frontispiece:
Self-Portrait, 1889
Oil on wood
31¼ × 20¼ in.
National Gallery of Art,
Washington,
Chester Dale Collection

Published by
Universe
381 Park Avenue South
New York, NY 10016
© 1989 Universe Books

89 90 91 92 93 : 10 9 8 7 6 5 4 3 2 1

Printed in Japan
Distributed to the trade by St. Martin's Press
Distributed in Canada by Book Center Inc., 1140 Beaulac Street,
Montreal, Quebec, H4R 1R8

gauguin

This publication presents thirteen fine examples of paintings and one print from Paul Gauguin's post-impressionist years (1887–1903). Drawn from the distinguished collections of six American museums—The Art Institute of Chicago, Indianapolis Museum of Art, National Gallery of Art, The Nelson-Atkins Museum of Art, The Toledo Museum of Art, and Worcester Art Museum— these brilliant and evocative works splendidly illustrate the scope of this French artist's mastery.

During the fifty-five years he lived, Gauguin was a merchant seaman, a stockbroker, a ditch digger, an artist, a writer, and a journalist. He was born in the midst of the 1848 revolutions, the only son of a left-wing journalist who was exiled from France in 1850. Gauguin spent his childhood first in Peru, where he lived with relatives, and then in the small city of Orléans, France. His remaining years were spent in a series of self-imposed exiles in Denmark, Brittany, Panama, Martinique, Tahiti, and finally, the Marquesan Islands.

january

1

2

3

Faaturuma
(The Dreamer), 1891
Oil on canvas
37¼ × 27 in.
The Nelson-Atkins
Museum of Art,
Kansas City, Missouri
(Nelson Fund)

4

january

5

6

7

8

9

10

11

january

12

13

14

15

16

17

18

january

19

20

21

22

23

24

25

Haystacks in Brittany, 1890
Oil on canvas
29¼ × 36⅞ in.
National Gallery of Art,
Washington,
Gift of the W. Averell
Harriman Foundation
in memory of Marie N.
Harriman

january

26

27

28

29

30

31

february

1

2

3

4

february

5

6

7

8

9

10

11

february

12

13

14

15

16

17

18

february

19

20

21

22

23

24

25

february

26

27

28

29

march

1

2

3

4

march

5

6

7

8

9

10

11

march

12

13

14

15

16

17

18

march

19

20

21

22

23

24

25

Landscape at Le Pouldu,
1890
Oil on canvas
$28\frac{7}{8} \times 36\frac{3}{8}$ in.
National Gallery of Art,
Washington, Collection of
Mr. and Mrs. Paul Mellon

march

26

27

28

29

30

31

april

1

2

3

4

april

5

6

7

8

9

10

11

12

13

14

15

16

17

18

april

19

20

21

22

23

24

25

26

27

28

29

30

may

1

2

3

Old Women at Arles, 1888
Oil on canvas
28¾ × 36⅕ in.
Courtesy of
The Art Institute of Chicago,
Mr. and Mrs. Lewis Larned
Coburn Memorial
Collection

4

may

5

6

7

8

9

10

11

may

12

13

14

15

16

17

18

may

19

20

21

22

23

24

25

may

26

27

28

29

30

31

june

1

2

3

4

june

5

6

7

8

9

10

11

june

12

13

14

15

16

17

18

june

19

20

21

22

23

24

25

26

27

28

29

30

july

1

2

3

Landscape near Arles, 1888
Oil on canvas
36 × 28¼ in.
© Indianapolis
Museum of Art,
Gift in Memory of
William Ray Adams

4

july

5

6

7

8

9

10

11

12

13

14

15

16

17

18

july

19

20

21

22

23

24

25

july

26

27

28

29

30

31

august

1

2

3

4

august

5

6

7

8

9

10

11

12

13

14

15

16

17

18

august

19

20

21

22

23

24

25

august

26

27

28

29

30

31

september

1

2

3

Parau na te Varua ino
(Words of the Devil), 1892
Oil on canvas
$36\frac{1}{8} \times 27$ in.
National Gallery of Art,
Washington,
Gift of the W. Averell
Harriman Foundation
in memory of Marie N.
Harriman

4

september

5

6

7

8

9

10

11

12

13

14

15

16

17

18

september

19

20

21

22

23

24

25

Fatata te Miti
(By the Sea), 1892
Oil on canvas
26¾ × 36 in.
National Gallery of Art,
Washington,
Chester Dale Collection

september

26

27

28

29

30

october

1

2

3

4

october

5

6

7

8

9

10

11

october

12

13

14

15

16

17

18

october

19

20

21

22

23

24

25

october

26

27

28

29

30

31

november

1

2

3

4

november

5

6

7

8

9

10

11

november

12

13

14

15

16

17

18

november

19

20

21

22

23

24

25

Te Faaturuma
(The Brooding Woman), 1891
Oil on canvas
35¾ × 26¾ in.
Worcester Art Museum

november

26

27

28

29

30

december

1

2

3

4

december

5

6

7

8

9

10

11

december

12

13

14

15

16

17

18

december

19

20

21

22

23

24

25

december

26

27

28

29

30

31

Little Breton Girls Dancing,
Pont-Aven, 1888
Oil on canvas
28¾ × 36½ in.
National Gallery of Art,
Washington, Collection of
Mr. and Mrs. Paul Mellon